DUDLEY SCHOOLS
LIBRARY SERVICE

KU-337-440

Schools Library and Information Services

S00000725211

GRAPHIC DISCOVERIES

SPECTACULAR SHIPWRECKS

by Gary Jeffrey

illustrated by Claudia Saraceni

FRANKLIN WATTS
LONDON•SYDNEY

First published in 2009 by Franklin Watts

Franklin Watts
338 Euston Road
London NW1 3BH

Franklin Watts Australia
Level 17/207 Kent Street
Sydney, NSW 2000

All rights reserved.

A CIP catalogue record for this book is available from the British Library.

Dewey number: 910.4'52

ISBN: 978 0 7496 9241 4

Franklin Watts is a division of Hachette Children's Books, an Hachette UK company.
www.hachette.co.uk

GRAPHIC DISCOVERIES: SPECTACULAR SHIPWRECKS produced for Franklin
Watts by David West Children's Books, 7 Princeton Court, 55 Felsham Road,
London SW15 1AZ

Copyright © 2009 David West Children's Books

Designed and produced by
David West Children's Books

Editor: Gail Bushnell

Photo credits:
4b&5t, 44all, 45t, NOAA; 6-7all, 45tr, OAR/National Undersea Research Program
(NURP); 45b, U.S. Navy photo by Photographer's Mate 1st Class Chadwick Vann

Printed in China

Website disclaimer:
Note to parents and teachers: Every effort has been made by the Publishers to ensure
that the websites in this book are suitable for children, that they are of the highest
educational value, and that they contain no inappropriate or offensive material.
However, because of the nature of the Internet, it is impossible to guarantee that the
contents of these sites will not be altered. We strongly advise that the Internet is
supervised by a responsible adult.

DUDLEY PUBLIC LIBRARIES
L
725211   SCH
J904

CONTENTS

HOW DO SHIPS GET WRECKED?

Ships are lost at sea for many reasons. Bad weather and striking underwater objects such as reefs or running aground in fog are the most obvious. Other reasons include sinking in battle, piracy, scuttling (sinking a ship on purpose by opening the seacocks), fire and navigational errors.

AMAZING AND BIZARRE

Other, less likely, causes range from simple carelessness to the very strange. In 1545, the English flagship, *Mary Rose*, capsized and sank as it advanced into battle. The inexperienced crew had left the gunports open. As the ship tipped sideways while changing direction, it filled with water which surged through the gunports as they went below the waterline.

Surprisingly, shipwrecks can sometimes appear on land. In 1883, a gigantic wave created by the eruption of the volcanic island Krakatoa lifted the steamship *Berouw* over 1.6 kilometres inland and 9 metres above sea level!

Ice can be a deadly shipwrecker, as most of it lies unseen underwater. In 1912, the *Titanic* struck an iceberg and sank within three hours. In 1915, the *Endurance*, on an expedition to Antarctica, was crushed by the force of the surrounding ice pack.

The most amazing cause for a shipwreck must go to the whaling ship *Essex,* from Nantucket, Massachusetts, in the USA. Destroyed in 1820, it sank after it was attacked by an 80-tonne sperm whale 3,200 kilometres from the west coast of South America.

A late 17th-century engraving shows a shipwreck and a whale. Apparently, fanciful tales of monsters attacking ships were not always make-believe.

Rocky coastlines with strong tides were very dangerous to shipping during the age of sail. People living in these places relied on shipwrecks as a source of income by collecting the goods that got washed ashore. They were known as wreckers (above).

A photograph (right) shows Endurance *trapped in the ice pack of the Weddell Sea, Antarctica. The expedition's leader, Shackleton, made a daring journey in a small boat to get help. All the crew members were eventually rescued.*

The remains of the most famous shipwreck ever, the Titanic *(left), were found in 1985.*

Diving suits, which had air pumped down to them through pipes from the surface (below), were replaced when the aqualung came along. Improvements to this design created the SCUBA - Self Contained Underwater Breathing Apparatus (above).

This 16th-century painting (above) shows a person being lowered into the sea in a diving bell. Diving machines, like this simple Lethbridge design (below) from 1715, allowed little time underwater as they had no fresh air supply.

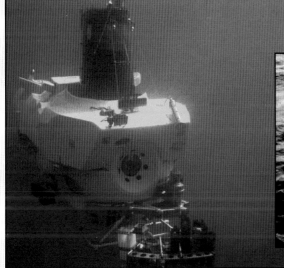

The Jim diving suit (above) protects the diver from pressure at depths of 600 metres or more.

Robert Ballard used submersibles, like Alvin (below), to visit the Titanic *wreck at a depth of 3,800 metres, in 1985.*

Remote-controlled subs with lights and cameras, like MIR (bottom right), explore wrecks without risking human life.

DIVING TECHNOLOGY

The technology that allows us to breathe underwater has greatly increased our ability to discover the hidden treasures beneath the waves.

EARLY DAYS

Divers began to explore the seabed in the 16th century, after the invention of a watertight diving bell. Soon after, leather diving suits with air pumped down tubes could be used at depths of 18 metres. By the 1830s, watertight diving suits allowed divers to work safely.

PRESSURE

Diving to greater depths created breathing problems until the aqualung was invented in 1943. To dive really deep, where the pressure can crush a person, special suits and submersibles are used, which allow scientists to go more than 4,200 metres deep.

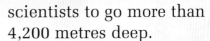

THE RAISING OF THE
MARY ROSE

> WE'VE A GOOD WIND BEHIND US, LADS!

19 JULY 1545, PORTSMOUTH HARBOUR. FLAGSHIP MARY ROSE LEADS OUT THE ENGLISH FLEET TO FIGHT THE FRENCH FLEET IN THE ENGLISH CHANNEL.

THE KING OF ENGLAND, HENRY VIII, WATCHES FROM THE SHORE...

> FAIR MARY ROSE, FIRST INTO THE FRAY - AS ALWAYS!

THE FRENCH HAVE 200 SHIPS RANGED AGAINST AN ENGLISH FORCE OF 80.

BOOOM!

> HARD-A-STARBOARD!

THE 34-YEAR-OLD SHIP DELIVERS A BROADSIDE.

KAABOOOOOM!

FIRE!

ANTI-BOARDING NETS COVER THE DECKS.

SHOUT TO THE HELMSMAN, HARD-A-PORT!

THE BOAT SWINGS AROUND TO OFFER HER OTHER CANNONS TO THE ENEMY.

THE WIND IS PICKING UP...

WAIT FOR THE ORDER TO FIRE!

MAY 1971.

HMM...AN OBJECT. WHAT IS IT?

MY GOODNESS, IT'S A TIMBER FRAME!

AND ANOTHER...AND ANOTHER. THIS *COULD* BE THE MARY ROSE!

BY MARCH 1979...

IT IS THE MARY ROSE - AN ALMOST PERFECTLY PRESERVED HALF A SHIP, FULL OF OBJECTS. AN AMAZING TIME CAPSULE OF DAYS GONE BY.

DR. MARGARET RULE, ARCHAEOLOGIST

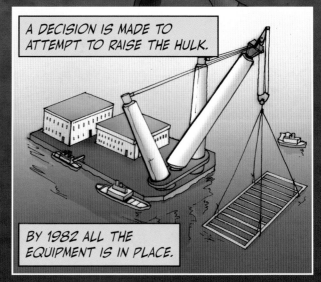

A DECISION IS MADE TO ATTEMPT TO RAISE THE HULK.

BY 1982 ALL THE EQUIPMENT IS IN PLACE.

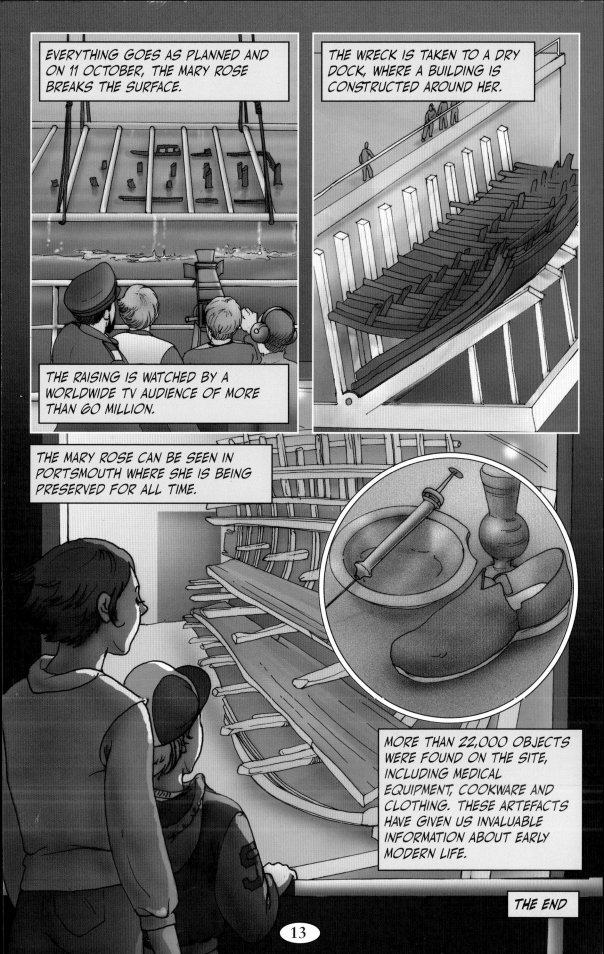

EVERYTHING GOES AS PLANNED AND ON 11 OCTOBER, THE MARY ROSE BREAKS THE SURFACE.

THE RAISING IS WATCHED BY A WORLDWIDE TV AUDIENCE OF MORE THAN 60 MILLION.

THE WRECK IS TAKEN TO A DRY DOCK, WHERE A BUILDING IS CONSTRUCTED AROUND HER.

THE MARY ROSE CAN BE SEEN IN PORTSMOUTH WHERE SHE IS BEING PRESERVED FOR ALL TIME.

MORE THAN 22,000 OBJECTS WERE FOUND ON THE SITE, INCLUDING MEDICAL EQUIPMENT, COOKWARE AND CLOTHING. THESE ARTEFACTS HAVE GIVEN US INVALUABLE INFORMATION ABOUT EARLY MODERN LIFE.

THE END

TITANIC

IN 1985, SCIENTIST DR ROBERT BALLARD LOCATED THE WRECK OF THE RMS TITANIC, THE GREAT LINER THAT SANK IN THE ATLANTIC OCEAN IN 1912.

ONE YEAR LATER HE RETURNS TO EXPLORE THE WRECK FURTHER...

SHE WAS STATE OF THE ART FOR HER TIME – DESIGNED TO BE PRACTICALLY 'UNSINKABLE'...

THEIR SUBMERSIBLE, ALVIN, HAS BEEN SPECIALLY ADAPTED TO WORK AT A DEPTH OF OVER 3.2 KILOMETRES.

I'VE ALWAYS WONDERED - WHY DID SHE SINK SO QUICKLY?

WITH BALLARD ARE PILOT RALPH HOLLIS AND COPILOT DUDLEY FOSTER.

WHAT WITH HAVING 16 WATER-TIGHT COMPARTMENTS INSIDE.

I'M AFRAID WE'LL HAVE TO REMAIN IN THE DARK FOR NOW. THE ACTUAL STRIKING POINT SEEMS TO BE BURIED.

LET'S CIRCLE AROUND BEFORE WE LAND.

...DEBRIS EXTENDS IN EVERY DIRECTION...

WHOA! WHAT IS THAT!

HHMN! EXCUSE ME, FOR A MOMENT I THOUGHT I SAW A BODY!

CAN YOU BACK US UP A LITTLE?

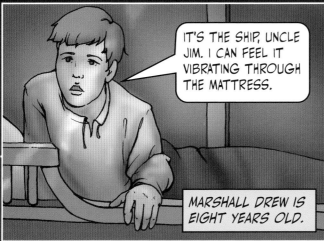

MARSHALL DREW IS EIGHT YEARS OLD.

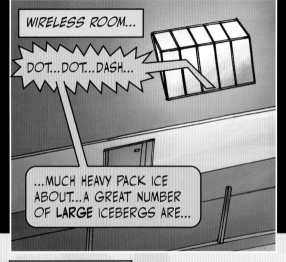

WIRELESS ROOM...

DOT...DOT...DASH...

...MUCH HEAVY PACK ICE ABOUT...A GREAT NUMBER OF **LARGE** ICEBERGS ARE...

...I'VE GOT SO MANY MESSAGES TO SEND – THIS WILL HAVE TO WAIT.

ON THE BRIDGE...

I *HAVE* TOLD THE CROW'S NEST TO KEEP THEIR EYES PEELED FOR GROWLERS*, SIR.

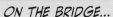

*SMALL ICEBERGS

JAMES MOODY IS TITANIC'S SIXTH OFFICER.

EXCELLENT. THEN WE SHALL MAINTAIN PRESENT COURSE AND SPEED.

WILLIAM MURDOCH IS TITANIC'S FIRST OFFICER.

AS LONG AS IT STAYS THIS CALM, THE LOOKOUTS WILL SPOT ANY HAZARDS IN PLENTY OF TIME.

...I ACTUALLY PREFER IT A BIT ROUGHER.

ON THE STARBOARD WING BRIDGE...

MR MURDOCH, WHAT HAVE WE STRUCK?

AN ICEBERG, SIR. I HARD-A-STARBOARDED AND REVERSED THE ENGINES, BUT SHE WAS TOO CLOSE...

FOURTH OFFICER BOXALL, MAKE AN INSPECTION OF THE FORWARD AREAS.

IN THE MAIL ROOM, LOWER DECK...

OH, MY, SHE'S TAKING ON WATER FAST!

THE FIRST FIVE COMPARTMENTS ARE FLOODED AS FAR AS BOILER ROOM SIX.

CAPTAIN SMITH!

MR ANDREWS*.

SHE CANNOT STAY AFLOAT WITH MORE THAN TWO COMPARTMENTS FLOODED.

*THOMAS ANDREWS, THE SHIP'S DESIGNER, WAS OVERSEEING THE MAIDEN VOYAGE.

SHEER WEIGHT OF WATER WILL PULL HER DOWN, CAUSING OVERTOPPING OF THE OTHER COMPARTMENTS ONE BY ONE. SHE WILL SINK AT THE HEAD.

HOW LONG HAVE WE GOT?

AN HOUR AND A HALF – TWO AT MOST.

12:15 PM...

UNCLE JIM, WAKE UP! THE SHIP'S STOPPED!

WHURRRRR...

WHAT'S GOING ON?

I DON'T KNOW, LOU, BUT PERHAPS...

KNOCK! KNOCK!

ALL PASSENGERS ARE TO GATHER ON THE BOAT DECK...

...WEARING THEIR LIFE JACKETS.

CLICK...CLICK....CLICK..

"COME...QUICKLY...DANGER ...SOS...FROM...TITANIC..."

LOOK AT ALL THAT STEAM!

THEY'RE EMPTYING THE BOILERS — IN CASE WE GO DOWN.

DISTRESS FLARE! IT MUST BE SERIOUS!

BOAT STATION 5, FIRST CLASS...

COME ALONG, LADIES!

THERE'S NO WAY I'M GOING ON THAT TINY LITTLE THING!

WE'RE MUCH SAFER STAYING HERE!

THE LADY'S RIGHT. I MEAN, GEE, HOW BAD CAN IT BE IF THE BAND'S STILL PLAYING?

BOAT STATION 14, 1:15 AM...

NUMBER SIXTEEN'S AWAY, SIR...

MOODY, WE HAVEN'T PUT A SINGLE OFFICER IN THE LAST FIVE BOATS.

YOU GO ON THIS ONE SIR. I'LL FIND ANOTHER BOAT.

HAROLD LOWE IS TITANIC'S FIFTH OFFICER.

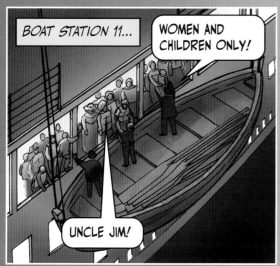

BOAT STATION 11...

WOMEN AND CHILDREN ONLY!

UNCLE JIM!

IT'S OK, I'LL SEE YOU BOTH SOON!

AT BOAT STATION 14...

HEY, YOU!

PLEASE!

YOU'VE GOT TEN SECONDS TO GET BACK ON THAT SHIP – WE'VE GOT WOMEN AND CHILDREN TO SAVE FIRST!

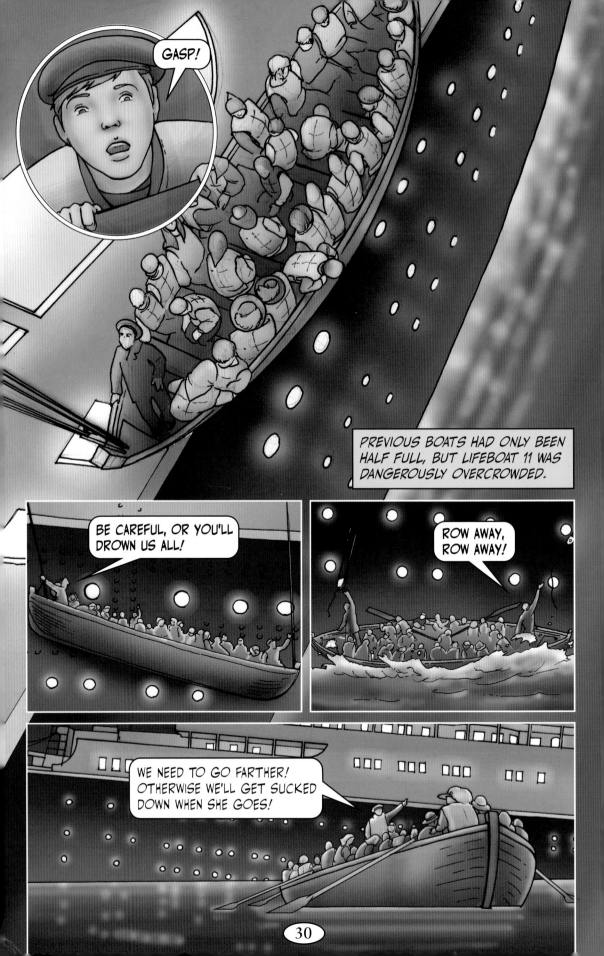

SCREEEHAAW!

GALOPH!

OUT OF 2,208 PEOPLE, ONLY 712 SURVIVED.

THE LOSS OF TITANIC WAS A HUGE BLOW TO AN AGE THAT BELIEVED IN THE POWER OF TECHNOLOGY OVER NATURE.

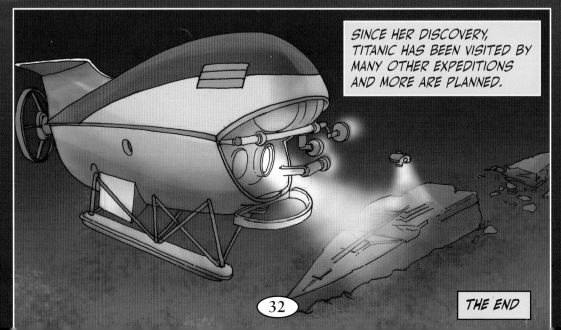

SINCE HER DISCOVERY, TITANIC HAS BEEN VISITED BY MANY OTHER EXPEDITIONS AND MORE ARE PLANNED.

THE END

THE SINKING OF THE BISMARCK

THE GERMAN BATTLESHIP BISMARCK, THE MOST POWERFUL WARSHIP EVER MADE, HAS LEFT HER BASE IN KIEL.

M O V I E T O N E
INTERNATIONAL WAR NEWS

IT IS THOUGHT THAT HER CAPTAIN, ERNST LINDEMANN, COULD BE LEADING AN ATLANTIC RAIDING PARTY UNDER THE COMMAND OF ADMIRAL GUNTHER LUTJENS.

THEIR MISSION WILL BE TO ATTACK THE CARGO SHIPS FERRYING SUPPLIES BETWEEN AMERICA AND BRITAIN.

THE BRITISH NAVY, UNDER ORDERS TO 'SINK THE BISMARCK!', WILL BE DOING ALL THEY CAN TO FIND THEM FIRST...

KORSFIJORD, NORWAY, 21 MAY 1941...

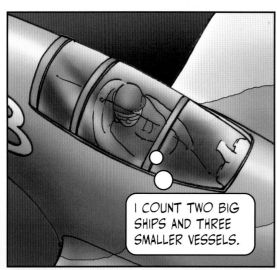

I COUNT TWO BIG SHIPS AND THREE SMALLER VESSELS.

COULD IT BE THE BISMARCK?

BRITISH NAVAL HIGH COMMAND.

SO IF THIS SECOND SHIP WITH BISMARCK *IS* THE HEAVY CRUISER PRINZ EUGEN...

...WE WILL SEND *OUR* HEAVY CRUISERS SUFFOLK AND NORFOLK TO PATROL THE BREAKOUT POINT.

SIR JOHN TOVEY IS THE COMMANDER-IN-CHIEF OF THE BRITISH HOME FLEET.

IF WE CAN SPOT THE ENEMY EARLY ENOUGH, WE'LL HAVE TIME TO GET OUR BIGGEST BATTLESHIPS INTO THE AREA...

DENMARK STRAIT

HOOD
PRINCE OF WALES

24 MAY, 5:45 AM.

THIS IS HOOD. WE HAVE ONE BATTLESHIP AND ONE CRUISER IN SIGHT, BEARING: 020°, DISTANCE: 13 MILES.

LOOKS LIKE IT'S GOING TO BE AN EVENLY MATCHED CONTEST.

INSTRUCT PRINCE OF WALES TO JOIN US IN FIRING AS SOON AS WE ARE IN RANGE.

REAR ADMIRAL LANCELOT HOLLAND IS CAPTAIN OF THE BATTLE CRUISER HMS HOOD.

HOOD LETS RIP...

KEEEHAAW!

THE BRITISH ARE COMING TOWARDS US, TRAVELLING FAST.

CAN YOU IDENTIFY THE LEAD SHIP?

YES...IT'S THE HOOD!

THE PRIDE OF THE BRITISH FLEET*!

*BEFORE BISMARCK, HOOD WAS THE BIGGEST WARSHIP AFLOAT.

SPLOOSH!

PLOSH!

WE WILL TARGET HOOD. ORDER PRINZ EUGEN TO DO THE SAME. FIRE AT WILL.

BISMARCK WAKES UP HER 380-MILLIMETRE GUNS.

KREEEHAAW!

KREEEHAAW!

KREEEHAAW!

KAABOFF!

GET THAT FIRE OUT!

ORDER TO BRING US ABOUT – LET'S THROW THE LOT AT THEM.

MEANWHILE, ON BISMARCK...

RANGE NINE MILES...

...POSITION 240°

ZZZZWEEEE!

BOOOM!

FIRE!

THE GERMAN SHELL BEARS DOWN ON THE VULNERABLE DECKS OF THE HOOD...

...AND HITS DIRECTLY AMIDSHIPS.

KERUMPH!

I THINK WE'VE GOT HER! WAIT...

PHSTUM!

KABAAAAH!

THE PRINCE OF WALES, FOLLOWING BEHIND, IS SHOWERED IN DEBRIS...

IN LESS THAN THREE MINUTES...

TAKE COVER!

...THE HOOD IS GONE.

BRITISH FLAGSHIP KING GEORGE V...

...PRINCE OF WALES RECEIVED SEVEN HITS, BUT HAS MANAGED TO RETREAT.

HOOD HAS GONE DOWN WITH THE LOSS OF 1,416 CREW – JUST THREE SURVIVORS.

THIS IS A MAJOR DISASTER...

MEANWHILE, ON THE BISMARCK...

AHA, THE DAMAGE REPORT!

WE HAVE RECEIVED THREE HITS, ONE SHELL PASSING THROUGH THE FORWARD TANKS. THE SHIP IS 3° DOWN BY THE BOW AND LISTING 9° TO PORT.

NO CASUALTIES.

PRINCE OF WALES HAS BEEN JOINED BY NORFOLK AND SUFFOLK. THEY ARE FOLLOWING BISMARCK AT LONG DISTANCE.

MEANWHILE, WE ARE CLOSING FROM THE SOUTHEAST AND FORCE H* IS COMING UP FROM GIBRALTAR. SO IT'S JUST A QUESTION OF WHO GETS TO THE ENEMY FIRST.

SIR! SUFFOLK REPORTS BISMARCK HAS MADE A SUDDEN CHANGE OF COURSE...

*AIRCRAFT CARRIER ARK ROYAL AND WARSHIPS RENOWN AND SHEFFIELD.

THE DIVERSION HAS WORKED, ADMIRAL, PRINZ EUGEN HAS SUCCESSFULLY DETACHED.

EXCELLENT! THEN WE WISH THEM *GOOD HUNTING!*

25 MAY, 12:00 PM...

SOLDIERS OF THE BATTLESHIP BISMARCK, YOU HAVE ACHIEVED GREAT FAME!

BECAUSE OF DAMAGE WE ARE ORDERED TO MAKE FOR A FRENCH HARBOUR. THE ENEMY FORCES WILL GATHER ALONG THE WAY AND TRY TO STOP US.

GERMANY IS WITH YOU! WE WILL FIRE UNTIL THE BARRELS GLOW AND THE LAST SHELL IS SPENT.

THE BATTLE CRY FROM NOW ON IS 'VICTORY OR DEATH'!

THE CARRIER ARK ROYAL, 26 MAY, 7:15 PM...

OK, MATE, CHOCKS AWAY!

WE MAY HAVE DAMAGED HER STEERING GEAR – SUFFOLK REPORTS...

SHE'S STEAMING IN CIRCLES – WE'VE GOT HER!

27 MAY, 8:43 ON BATTLESHIP RODNEY...

BISMARCK SIGHTED... RANGE 12 MILES.

RODNEY FIRES.

KAROOM

SIR, NORFOLK'S HERE TO HELP US OUT.

TELL THEM WE'RE GLAD TO HAVE THEM ALONG.

8:49...

HNNNH, WE'RE HIT!

RETURN FIRE! RETURN FIRE!

SHE'S ONLY MAKING SEVEN KNOTS.

THEY'RE LIKE SITTING DUCKS!

KABWAAAAAMM!

IN 2002, MOVIEMAKER JAMES CAMERON FILMED THE BISMARCK AND MADE AN INVESTIGATION...

LET'S SEE IF IT'S TRUE THAT SHE WAS SCUTTLED BY HER OWN SAILORS.

HEY, THERE'S A BULGE! - PROBABLY FROM A TORPEDO IMPACT.

YES, BUT LOOK, THE ARMOURED BELT BEHIND IS UNDAMAGED.

AMAZING! I THINK SHE COULD HAVE FLOATED FOR AT LEAST ANOTHER DAY!

ONE THING'S FOR SURE - THEY DON'T BUILD SHIPS LIKE THIS ANYMORE!

THE END

43

UNDERSEA ARCHAEOLOGY

Ancient shipwrecks can be a valuable source of historical information. Finding and preserving the finds requires expert knowledge and modern technology.

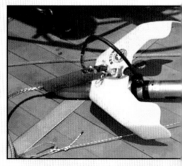

The side-scan sonar tow vehicle (above) sends data back to the ship's computer (below).

FINDING WRECKS

Usually historical evidence such as eyewitness accounts gives a rough idea of where a wreck might be. When they are near the site, wreck hunters use remote sensing to detect objects without having to enter the water themselves. Magnetometers can sense iron objects like nails and anchors even if they are buried beneath sediment. Unlike normal sonar, which scans the seabed from the top, side-scan sonar sends very realistic images. Sub-bottom profilers enable the viewer to see below the sediment and detect non-metallic objects that are fully buried.

The side-scan sonar can give a very clear picture of a wreck (below).

RECORDING AND PRESERVING

Once a wreck has been discovered, it has to be carefully recorded by divers or by remote-controlled submersibles. A grid of wire or metal tubes is constructed over the wreck and drawings and photos record the finds before they are collected. The removal of items, which may appear well preserved, from the seabed, can set off a reaction that destroys them when they are exposed to the air. When items are removed from the site, they must go straight to laboratories where they can be preserved.

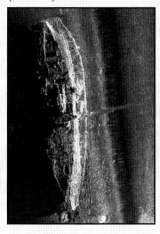

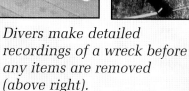

Divers make detailed recordings of a wreck before any items are removed (above right).

Sometimes sediment has to be removed from a buried wreck using a tube attached to a suction pump (right).

Items rescued from the sunken American civil war-era, ironclad USS Monitor have to be carefully treated to preserve them (below).

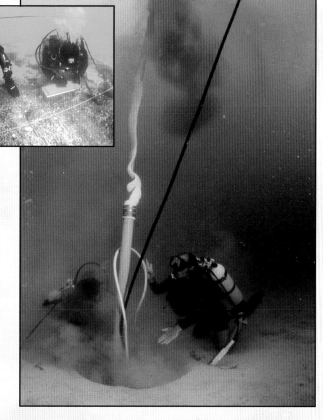

GLOSSARY

Antarctica A continent around the South Pole entirely covered in ice.

archaeology The study of human history and prehistory through the digging up of sites that contain remains.

artefacts Man-made objects of historical interest.

capsize To overturn in water, usually resulting in a ship sinking.

compartment A separate section inside a ship.

debris Scattered pieces of a wreck.

diving bell An open-bottomed barrel or bell-shaped vessel that was waterproof. A diver could breathe the air inside while underwater. Later versions had air pumped down to them through a tube from a boat on the surface.

engraving An early form of print on paper, made from a plate of metal or block of wood that has had the image cut out or 'engraved'.

expedition A journey with a purpose, usually exploration or scientific.

fanciful Ideas or thoughts made up, that are not based on the truth.

gunports The openings in the side of a ship through which the guns fired. Gunports had watertight hatches.

hard–a–starboard To turn a boat quickly to the left, or port, by turning the wheel to the left. On early ships the tiller would be pushed to the right (starboard) in order to turn the ship left.

ice pack A large area of floating pieces of ice that are driven together to make one large floating piece. Also called pack ice.

inexperience A lack of knowledge or skill.

ironclad A 19th-century warship made of iron or made of wood covered with plates of iron.

navigational errors Mistakes made in steering a ship in the correct direction.

obvious Clear or easy to understand.

preserving To keep the condition of something as it is.

remote-controlled To control something, like a submersible, from a distance using electronic signals such as radio waves.

seacock A valve in the hull of a vessel used to let in water.

sediment A layer of fine material, which can be several metres thick, that has sunk to the seabed.

sonar A device used to 'see' things underwater by sending a sound signal and measuring its return. From SOund, NAvigation and Ranging.

submersible A small craft designed to explore underwater.

FOR MORE INFORMATION

ORGANISATIONS

The Mary Rose
Portsmouth Historic Dockyard
Visitor Centre
Victory Gate
HM Naval Base
Portsmouth PO1 3LJ
02392 839766
Website: www.maryrose.org

Fort Grey & Shipwreck Museum
Candie Gardens
St Peter Port
GY1 1UG
Guernsey
01481 706969
Website: www.museum.guernsey.net/fortgrey.htm

FURTHER READING

Hook, Jason. *Shipwrecks* (History Mysteries). London: Belitha Press Ltd, 2001.

Malam, John. *Titanic: Shipwrecks and Sunken Treasure.* London: Dorling Kindersley Publishers Ltd, 2003.

Platt, Richard. *Shipwreck* (Eyewitness Guides). London: Dorling Kindersley Publishers Ltd, 1997.

Ross, Stewart. *Shipwrecks* (Amazing History). London: Franklin Watts, 2007.

INDEX